# Amazing
# Addition & Subtract

## Paul Broadbent

In a hidden cave, far away in a magical land, lives a wise wizard, called Whimstaff. Every now and again, he searches for a young apprentice, so he can pass on his magical Maths powers. And this time, Whimstaff has chosen you!

Whimstaff shares the cave with a goblin and a little, red dragon. Pointy, the goblin, is very clever. The dragon, called Miss Snufflebeam, breathes small puffs of fire. She is clumsy and often loses the wizard's magical letters and numbers.

Pointy has two greedy, pet frogs, called Mugly and Bugly, who are very lazy and spend most of their time croaking, eating and sleeping. But every so often, they amaze Pointy by helping with an exercise!

Wizard Whimstaff and his friends are very happy in their cave, solving Maths problems. Join them on a magical quest to become a fully qualified Maths wizard!

## ⭐ Contents

*Letts*

# Terrific Totals

Hello! I'm Wizard Whimstaff and I'm here to help you learn maths. To become a maths master like me, it's useful to know the number facts for different totals.

Abracadabra! Here are all the addition facts for 14.

0 + 14   1 + 13   2 + 12   3 + 11
4 + 10   5 + 9   6 + 8   7 + 7

Just do the best you can on the tasks, my apprentice.

⭐ **Task 1** These books of mine can only be opened with maths magic! All you have to do is write all the addition facts for each number and then – Allakazan! The books can be opened!

**a** 16      **b** 17      **c** 11      **d** 12

| a | | b | | c | | d | |
|---|---|---|---|---|---|---|---|
| ☐ + ☐ | | ☐ + ☐ | | ☐ + ☐ | | ☐ + ☐ | |
| ☐ + ☐ | | ☐ + ☐ | | ☐ + ☐ | | ☐ + ☐ | |
| ☐ + ☐ | | ☐ + ☐ | | ☐ + ☐ | | ☐ + ☐ | |
| ☐ + ☐ | | ☐ + ☐ | | ☐ + ☐ | | ☐ + ☐ | |
| ☐ + ☐ | | ☐ + ☐ | | ☐ + ☐ | | ☐ + ☐ | |
| ☐ + ☐ | | ☐ + ☐ | | ☐ + ☐ | | ☐ + ☐ | |
| ☐ + ☐ | | ☐ + ☐ | | | | ☐ + ☐ | |
| ☐ + ☐ | | ☐ + ☐ | | | | | |
| ☐ + ☐ | | ☐ + ☐ | | | | | |

**Task 2** Hey Presto! Here's a puzzle I thought you might enjoy. Write the answers to these doubles as words and you will find the sorcerer's secret number in the shaded boxes.

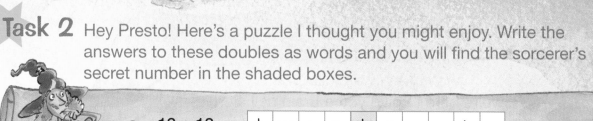

**a** 13 + 13 = `t` `w` `e` `n` `t` `y` `-` `s` `i` `x`

**b** 10 + 10 =

**c** 12 + 12 =

**d** 14 + 14 =

**e** 18 + 18 =

**f** 15 + 15 =

**g** 17 + 17 =

**h** 16 + 16 =

**i** 11 + 11 =

**j** 19 + 19 =

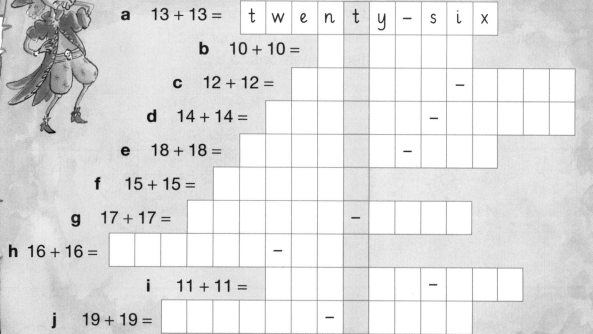

# Sorcerer's Skill Check

Miss Snufflebeam has made some of the numbers on these pages disappear! Can you help and write the missing numbers to make 50 and 100?

**50**

30 + [ ]     [ ] + 25

15 + [ ]

[ ] + 28     14 + [ ]

[ ] + 41     19 + [ ]

**100**

[ ] + 50     75 + [ ]

[ ] + 40

80 + [ ]     [ ] + 38

64 + [ ]     [ ] + 71

**Cabradababa! Add a gold star to your certificate! You'll be as brainy as Wizard Whimstaff soon!**

# Astonishing Addition

We're Mugly and Bugly and we're here to give you a brain cell alert! How would you work out 38 + 46?

Slurp … When adding two numbers in your head, here are some different methods to try.

40 add 46 is 86.
86 take away 2 is 84.

38 add 40 is 78.
78 + 6 is 84.

30 + 40 is 70.
8 + 6 is 14.
70 + 14 is 84.

8 + 6 is 14.
30 + 40 is 70.
70 + 14 is 84.

**Task 1** We've done enough work. Is it time for a snooze yet? We'll leave you to work these out in your head and write the answers.

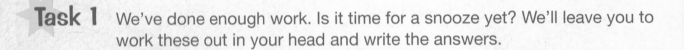

**a** 42 + 29 = ☐        **b** 19 + 23 = ☐        **c** 44 + 32 = ☐

**d** 28 + 27 = ☐        **e** 47 + 26 = ☐

**f** 39 + 43 = ☐        **g** 25 + 46 = ☐        **h** 17 + 35 = ☐

**i** 37 + 24 = ☐        **j** 36 + 18 = ☐

**Task 2** Burp! We only get dinner once these cauldron calculations are completed and add up. The cauldron on top is the total of the two cauldrons below.

82

45  37

31  14  23

**a**

32  19  17

**b**

23  24  18

**c**
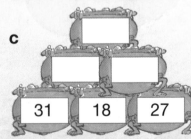

31  18  27

4

**Task 3** Here are some more cauldrons for you to do!

a

| 19 | 23 | 25 |

b

| 32 | 13 | 41 |

c

| 13 | 21 | 17 |

**Task 4** These tricky cluster of clouds both have a top total of 100, but you have to make each cluster different.

100

100

# Sorcerer's Skill Check

Use mental methods and colour pairs of spoons that have the same answer. Careful – if you get too clever, we might have to call you Pointy!

**a** 32 + 19

**d** 38 + 29

**b** 27 + 24

**e** 32 + 24

**c** 29 + 27

**f** 32 + 35

You can now add your gold star to your certificate, young apprentice! Super!

5

# Amazing Adding

I'm Pointy, Wizard Whimstaff's clever assistant.

Here are two super ways to try when adding three numbers in your head.

Start with the largest number and then add the other two.

28 add 13 is 41, then 41 add 7 is 48. Super!

28
7
13
Total 48

Always look for pairs that are easy to add.

13 add 7 is 20, then 20 add 28 is 48. Super!

It's easy when you know how!

**Task 1** Practice makes perfect! So to work, young apprentice, and write the total for each wizard hat!

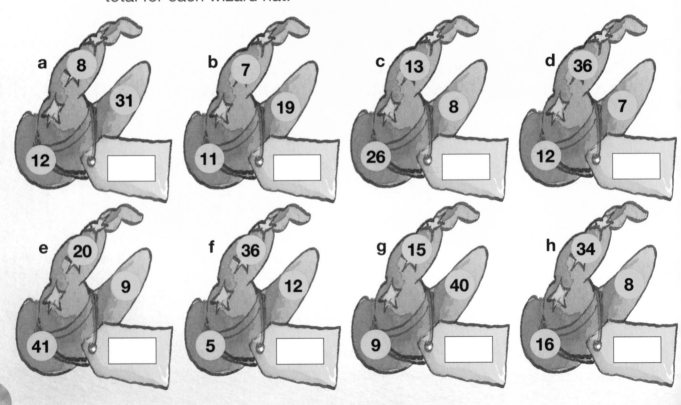

a  8  31  12  ☐

b  7  19  11  ☐

c  13  8  26  ☐

d  36  7  12  ☐

e  20  9  41  ☐

f  36  12  5  ☐

g  15  40  9  ☐

h  34  8  16  ☐

**Task 2** Did you know that wizards love sweets? I keep a chart to show how much Wizard Whimstaff spends on sweets each day. Can you add the total for each day?

| Monday | Tuesday | Wednesday | Thursday | Friday |
|--------|---------|-----------|----------|--------|
| 17p 9p 28p | 36p 9p 13p | 34p 11p 17p | 36p 17p 11p | 34p 13p 11p |
| Total ___ p | Total ___ p | Total ___ p | Total ___ p | Total ___ p |

**Task 3** On Saturdays, Wizard Whimstaff always spends exactly 50p. Super! Choose 3 sweets from the chart above that he could buy for exactly 50p.

Write the price on the sweets for Saturday and colour them.

Saturday

Total 50p

# Sorcerer's Skill Check

Now cast a circle around three touching numbers that total 20. Two have been done to get you started! You'll soon get the hang of it!

| 8 | 4 | 6 | 7 | 7 | 5 | 2 | 3 | 8 |
|---|---|---|---|---|---|---|---|---|
| 3 | 7 | 9 | 4 | 1 | 8 | 6 | 9 | 2 |
| 9 | 3 | 1 | 3 | 5 | 2 | 6 | 2 | 3 |
| 4 | 8 | 8 | 2 | 6 | 1 | 3 | 8 | 1 |
| 1 | 9 | 5 | 6 | 9 | 5 | 2 | 5 | 7 |

How many did you find?

[ ]

**Well completed! Add a gold star to your certificate.**

# Wonderful Written Methods

I'm Miss Snufflebeam
and I get very confused!

Help! Larger numbers are too difficult to add in my head.
I know – I'll use a written method.

$$48 \longrightarrow \text{is} \longrightarrow 40 + 8$$
$$+87 \longrightarrow \text{is} \longrightarrow 80 + 7$$
$$120 + 15 = 135$$

Cabradababa! This method can be written as:

$$\begin{array}{r} 48 \\ +87 \\ \hline 135 \\ \tiny{1} \end{array}$$  Add the units first and carry any tens to the next column.

⭐ **Task 1**  My head hurts! Can you use my wonderful written method to answer
these? You might be clever enough to work some out in your head.
If so, colour the star.

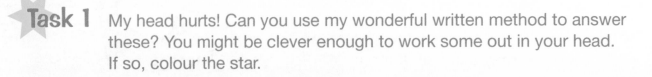

a   54
   +32   ✦

b   72
   +53   ✦

c   65
   +39   ✦

d   81
   +77   ✦

e   57
   +94   ✦

f   67
   +84   ✦

g   83
   +79   ✦

h   94
   +68   ✦

i   85
   +76   ✦

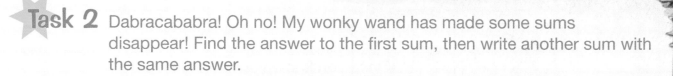

## Task 2
Dabracababra! Oh no! My wonky wand has made some sums disappear! Find the answer to the first sum, then write another sum with the same answer.

a
```
    5 9
  + 8 4      +
  _____    _____

  _____    _____
```

b
```
    7 6
  + 4 8      +
  _____    _____

  _____    _____
```

c
```
    6 7
  + 9 2      +
  _____    _____

  _____    _____
```

d
```
    5 4
  + 1 3 9    +
  _____    _____

  _____    _____
```

e
```
    5 8
  + 1 6 1    +
  _____    _____

  _____    _____
```

f
```
    7 7
  + 1 4 6    +
  _____    _____

  _____    _____
```

g
```
    1 6 2
  + 1 3 5    +
  _____    _____

  _____    _____
```

h
```
    1 2 7
  + 1 6 5    +
  _____    _____

  _____    _____
```

i
```
    1 5 8
  + 1 6 9    +
  _____    _____

  _____    _____
```

## Sorcerer's Skill Check

Rabracadada! Oh dear, the stars have floated away from the sums.
Write in the missing numbers by matching each star to a sum space.

5  8  2  9  6  5  6  3  1  7

a
```
  ⭐ 7
+   6 8
_____
  9 ⭐
```

b
```
  ⭐ 8
+   7 ⭐
_____
  1 0 9
```

c
```
  5 ⭐
+   9 4
_____
  1 ⭐ 0
```

d
```
  ⭐ 3
+   7 ⭐
_____
  1 4 1
```

e
```
    5 4
+   ⭐ 3
_____
  1 4 ⭐
```

Slurp! We must have been snoozing.
Another gold star for you, clever clogs!

# Magnificent Multiples of Ten

Once you know your addition bonds,
it's easy to add multiples of 10
to other numbers.

Hey Presto! Look at the patterns in these.

| | | | | |
|---|---|---|---|---|
| 5 + 9 | = 14 | 9 + 8 | = 17 |
| 50 + 90 | = 140 | 90 + 80 | = 170 |
| 500 + 900 | = 1400 | 93 + 80 | = 173 |

Don't worry if it seems hard at first.

**Task 1** Abracadabra! Have a go at this exercise and write the answers for these.

**a** 4 + 7 = ☐    **b** 12 + 6 = ☐    **c** 9 + 14 = ☐

40 + 70 = ☐    120 + 60 = ☐    90 + 140 = ☐

400 + 700 = ☐    1200 + 600 = ☐    900 + 1400 = ☐

**Task 2** These are slightly different – just do the best you can on this task.

**a** 9 + 6 = ☐    **b** 8 + 3 = ☐    **c** 7 + 8 = ☐

90 + 60 = ☐    80 + 30 = ☐    70 + 80 = ☐

95 + 60 = ☐    82 + 30 = ☐    70 + 84 = ☐

**Task 3** Remember to use the magnificent multiples of 10 method to answer these.

**a** 15 + 7 = ☐    **b** 19 + 4 = ☐    **c** 14 + 6 = ☐

150 + 70 = ☐    190 + 40 = ☐    140 + 60 = ☐

152 + 70 = ☐    193 + 40 = ☐    140 + 63 = ☐

**Task 4** Can you help me by writing the amounts and the totals for these pairs of potions? Allakazan! I've done the first one for you.

800 ml + 1300 ml = 2100 ml

**a**

**b**

[____] ml + [____] ml = [____] ml    [____] ml + [____] ml = [____] ml

## Sorcerer's Skill Check

I've invited two friends for tea. Can you answer these and use the code wheel to find their names?

**a** 1200 + 500 = [1700]  H

500 + 800 = [____]  ___

1100 + 800 = [____]  ___

400 + 1500 = [____]  ___

900 + 400 = [____]  ___

800 + 900 = [____]  ___

**b** 800 + 800 = [____]  ___

1400 + 300 = [____]  ___

1100 + 200 = [____]  ___

600 + 800 = [____]  ___

1300 + 500 = [____]  ___

600 + 1300 = [____]  ___

Code wheel: 1700, 1800, 1400, O, H, R, A, N, 1300, S, 1900, 1600

Cabradababa! You're very clever. You deserve another gold star!

# Creaking Coins

I look after Wizard Whimstaff's money for him.

Here's a super way to add coins – start with the highest value coins.

Remember £1 = 100p, so £2.35 is the same as 235p.

This is how I add these coins.

£1 + £1 = £2
£2 + 50p = £2.50
£2.50 + 20p = £2.70
£2.70 + 10p + 10p = £2.90
£2.90 + 2p = £2.92
The total is £2.92

**Task 1** Now you have a try! Practise your magic and write the totals in each of these wizard wallets.

a

Total £ [ ]

b

Total £ [ ]

c

Total £ [ ]

d

Total £ [ ]

**Task 2** Wizard Whimstaff wants to buy each of these books. I have to give him the correct coins to make sure he has exactly the right amount. Can you help me and write amounts on each coin?

a £1.85

b £2.35

Book of 9 Spells

c £1.43

d £3.55

e £2.17

f £2.72

# Sorcerer's Skill Check

I'm off to the Sorcerer's Superstore and I need exactly £3 in each of my wizard wallets. Can you use only these coins to make £3 in 4 different ways? You can use each coin more than once and you can have any number of coins in each wallet.

a

b

c

d

Well completed, young apprentice!
Add a gold star to your certificate.

# Apprentice Wizard Challenge 1

## Challenge 1
The numbers on the opposite points of these stars, when added together, make the centre number. Write the missing numbers.

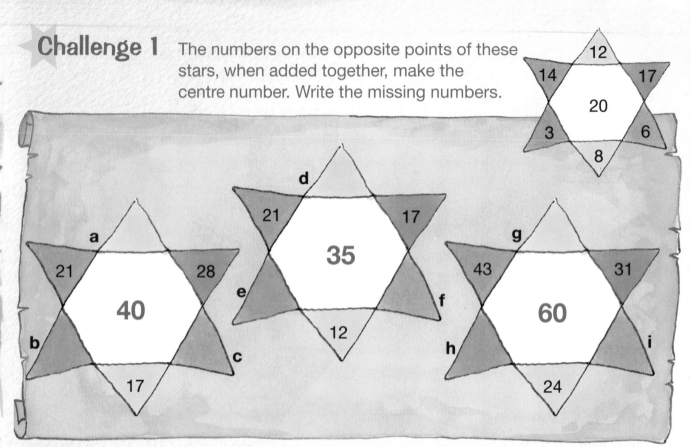

## Challenge 2
Write the totals for each of these.

**a** What is 48 add 24? ▢

**b** What is the total of 35 and 29? ▢

**c** What is the sum of 51 and 34? ▢

**d** Add together 26 and 37. ▢

## Challenge 3
Write the totals for each of these wizard hats.

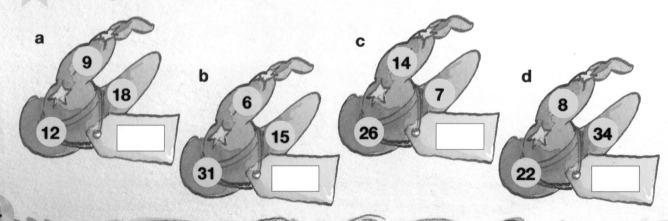

14

## Challenge 4 Write the answer to each of these:

a  29
  +56
  ____

b  34
  +73
  ____

c  27
  +68
  ____

d  47
  +58
  ____

e  39
  +67
  ____

f  223
  +106
  ____

g  184
  +223
  ____

h  337
  +259
  ____

i  256
  +169
  ____

## Challenge 5 Write the total weight of each pair of potion pots on the scales.

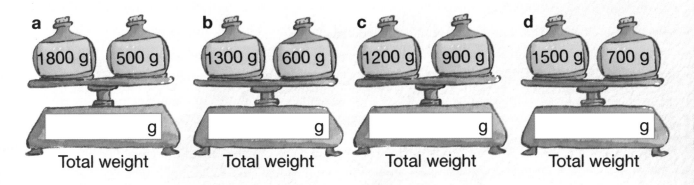

a  1800 g  500 g

_____ g

Total weight

b  1300 g  600 g

_____ g

Total weight

c  1200 g  900 g

_____ g

Total weight

d  1500 g  700 g

_____ g

Total weight

## Challenge 6 Draw extra coins to make each wizard wallet add up to £2.

a  Draw three more coins.

b  Draw five more coins.

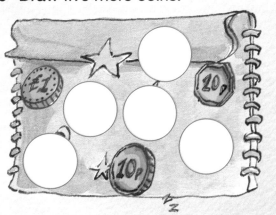

**Croak! We're off for a snooze while you get yourself a gold star.**

# Creepy Calculations

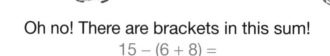

Oh no! There are brackets in this sum!
$15 - (6 + 8) =$

Cabradababa! If there are brackets in a sum, you must remember to work out the brackets first.

**Begin with the brackets!**

$$15 - (6 + 8) \quad = \quad ?$$
$$\text{so, } (6 + 8) \quad = \quad 14$$
$$15 - \underline{14} \quad = \quad 1$$

If there are no brackets, you work out the sum in the order it's written.
$15 - 6 + 8 = 17$

**Task 1** My head hurts – these brackets are driving me batty! Can you answer these?

**a** $16 - 11 - 4 =$ ☐  **b** $20 + (15 - 7) =$ ☐  **c** $21 - (4 + 7) =$ ☐

$16 - (11 - 4) =$ ☐  $20 + 15 - 7 =$ ☐  $21 - 4 + 7 =$ ☐

**Task 2** Rabracadada! It's the Annual Bat Race! To enter, you have to follow the trail and complete the calculations until you're back at the start. Good luck!

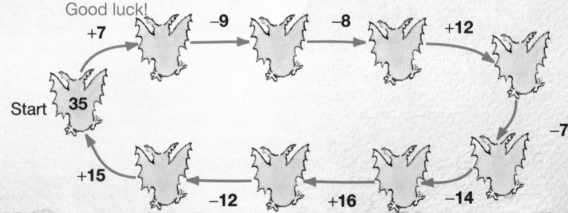

Start **35**

+7   −9   −8   +12   −7

+15   −12   +16   −14

**Task 3** Oh no! These are too difficult for me. You're clever – can you answer them?

**a** $(11 - 5) + (5 - 2)$ =

**b** $(6 + 4) - (10 - 5)$ =

**c** $(12 + 3) + (5 + 7)$ =

**d** $(15 - 4) - (7 + 2)$ =

**e** $(9 + 4) + (17 - 11)$ =

**f** $(17 - 4) - (13 - 6)$ =

Remember, begin with brackets! Work out **both** brackets first.

**Task 4** Rabracadada! Oops! My clumsy spell has made the + and – signs disappear! Write in the missing + and – signs to make all the answers 24.

| | | | | | | | | | |
|---|---|---|---|---|---|---|---|---|---|
| **a** | 19 | | 4 | | 1 | **g** | 31 | | 9 | | 2 |
| **b** | 8 | | 5 | | 21 | **h** | 48 | | 14 | | 10 |
| **c** | 12 | | 21 | | 9 | **i** | 17 | | 19 | | 12 |
| **d** | 32 | | 6 | | 2 | **j** | 12 | | 7 | | 5 |
| **e** | 17 | | 9 | | 2 | **k** | 18 | | 17 | | 11 |
| **f** | 13 | | 6 | | 5 | **l** | 13 | | 7 | | 18 |

$= 24$

## Sorcerer's Skill Check

You're getting clever with calculations! Please will you complete these.

**a** $19 + 4 + 8$ =

**b** $16 + (8 - 3)$ =

**c** $23 - (12 - 4)$ =

**d** $(17 + 4) - 3$ =

**e** $17 + 3 - 2$ =

**f** $(18 - 6) + 9$ =

You're a wonderful wizard in the making.
Add a gold star to your certificate. Super!

# Dazzling Differences

Croak …

To find the difference between two numbers, count on to the next 10, then count on to the largest number.

**What is the difference between 27 and 70?**

27  + 3  30  + 40  70

The difference is 43.

Slurp! The difference between Pointy and us is that he enjoys all this work!

**Task 1** We've got our frog friends to help you find the differences. Use our counting on method by writing the missing numbers under the frogs, and then write the difference between the two larger lily pad numbers.

Difference

a   38   +   40   +   80

b   46   +   50   +   90

c   25   +   30   +   60

**Task 2** Brain cell alert! Write all the missing numbers and find the differences, while we have a snooze!

Difference

a   34   +   +   60

b   52   +   +   70

c   67   +   +   100

18

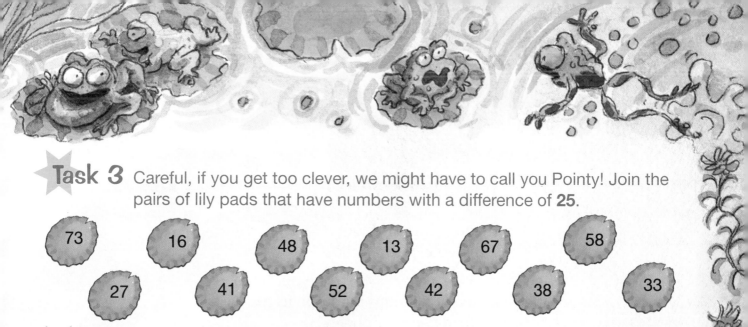

## Task 3

Careful, if you get too clever, we might have to call you Pointy! Join the pairs of lily pads that have numbers with a difference of **25**.

73    16    48    13    67    58

27    41    52    42    38    33

## Task 4

Burp! Can you find these differences?

**a**  50 g   23 g

Difference ☐ g

**c**  62 g   28 g

Difference ☐ g

**b** 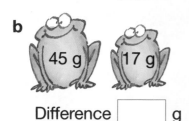 45 g   17 g

Difference ☐ g

**d**  49 g   26 g

Difference ☐ g

## Sorcerer's Skill Check

Wizard Whimstaff needs these difference grids completed. We're off for a snack, so could you write in all the differences for us?

**a**

| −  | 47 | 61 | 58 |
|----|----|----|----|
| 32 |    |    |    |
| 21 |    |    |    |
| 28 |    |    |    |

**b**

| −  | 41 | 52 | 48 |
|----|----|----|----|
| 13 |    |    |    |
| 22 |    |    |    |
| 25 |    |    |    |

Another gold star for another fine piece of work.
Well done, young apprentice!

# Scintillating Subtraction

How would you work out 84 − 39, my young apprentice?

When subtracting two numbers in your head, there are many different methods to try. Take a look at these.

### Allakazan!

84 take away 40 is 44.
Add 1 more is 45.

### Hey Presto!

84 take away 30 is 54.
Take away another 9 is 45.

### Abracadabra!

Counting on from 39 to 40 is 1, and 40 on to 84 is 44. 44 + 1 is 45.

**Task 1**  Try working these out in your head. Don't worry if it seems hard at first.

a  78 − 35 = ☐          d  57 − 28 = ☐          g  49 − 24 = ☐

b  81 − 48 = ☐          e  63 − 37 = ☐          h  72 − 46 = ☐

c  94 − 59 = ☐          f  35 − 18 = ☐          i  76 − 57 = ☐

**Task 2**  Now have a go at this exercise. You can use different methods for each question.

a  45 − 28 = ☐          d  62 − 14 = ☐          g  96 − 59 = ☐

b  33 − 17 = ☐          e  84 − 51 = ☐          h  71 − 25 = ☐

c  58 − 29 = ☐          f  66 − 47 = ☐          i  82 − 36 = ☐

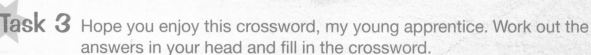

## Task 3
Hope you enjoy this crossword, my young apprentice. Work out the answers in your head and fill in the crossword.

| Across | | Down | |
|---|---|---|---|
| **a** | 53 – 26 | **a** | 44 – 22 |
| **c** | 60 – 21 | **b** | 36 – 21 |
| **d** | 56 – 21 | **c** | 59 – 23 |
| **e** | 83 – 19 | **d** | 42 – 11 |
| **g** | 65 – 24 | **f** | 60 – 15 |
| **i** | 41 – 26 | **g** | 72 – 26 |
| **j** | 58 – 11 | **h** | 64 – 27 |
| **l** | 58 – 26 | **i** | 36 – 18 |
| **m** | 46 – 37 | **j** | 66 – 24 |
| **n** | 68 – 40 | **k** | 57 – 9 |

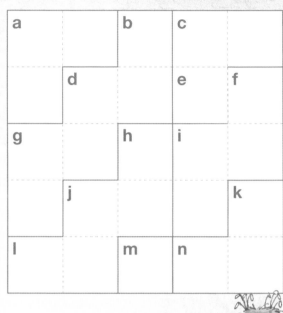

## Sorcerer's Skill Check

Write what happens to each of these.

**a**   45   –   ☐   =   23

**b**   53   –   ☐   =   38

**c**   60   –   ☐   =   36

**d**   35   –   ☐   =   12

Abracadada! You can now add your gold star to your certificate!

21

# Sparkling Subtraction

When subtracting large numbers that you can't work out in your head, use a written method. Super!

Learn to change tens to units and hundreds to tens.

$$\begin{array}{r} 3\,\overset{7}{\cancel{8}}\,\overset{16}{\cancel{6}} \\ -1\,5\,8 \\ \hline 2\,2\,8 \end{array}$$

- Change a ten for units.
- Subtract the units.
- Subtract the tens.
- Subtract the hundreds.

It's easy when you know how!

**Task 1**  Now you have a try and answer these. Colour the star if you can work it out in your head.

a
$$\begin{array}{r} 9\,6 \\ -3\,1 \\ \hline \end{array}$$

b
$$\begin{array}{r} 8\,7 \\ -4\,3 \\ \hline \end{array}$$

c
$$\begin{array}{r} 8\,4 \\ -3\,8 \\ \hline \end{array}$$

d
$$\begin{array}{r} 6\,3 \\ -3\,6 \\ \hline \end{array}$$

e
$$\begin{array}{r} 9\,4 \\ -4\,8 \\ \hline \end{array}$$

**Task 2**  Practice makes perfect! Answer these and you'll soon get the hang of it!

| a | b | c | d | e |
|---|---|---|---|---|
| $\begin{array}{r} 1\,2\,8 \\ -4\,7 \\ \hline \end{array}$ | $\begin{array}{r} 2\,4\,1 \\ -1\,0\,7 \\ \hline \end{array}$ | $\begin{array}{r} 3\,5\,3 \\ -1\,3\,9 \\ \hline \end{array}$ | $\begin{array}{r} 2\,3\,7 \\ -1\,4\,2 \\ \hline \end{array}$ | $\begin{array}{r} 2\,8\,4 \\ -1\,9\,6 \\ \hline \end{array}$ |

**Task 3** Use this written method to answer these subtractions. Remember to line up the hundreds, tens and units columns. Super!

**a** 5 4 3 – 1 6 2 = ☐

**b** 4 0 8 – 2 3 7 = ☐

**c** 6 5 1 – 3 6 9 = ☐

Working out area:

# Sorcerer's Skill Check

Mugly and Bugly, the lazy frogs, have let the star numbers float away! Write in the missing numbers, matching each floating star to the right subtraction sum.

⭐8 ⭐5 ⭐2 ⭐0 ⭐7 ⭐1 ⭐3 ⭐6 ⭐9 ⭐4

**a**
```
  2 ⭐ 8
– 1 3 9
───────
  1 3 ⭐
```

**b**
```
  2 6 ⭐
– ⭐ 4 3
───────
  1 1 7
```

**c**
```
  ⭐ 8 6
– 1 ⭐ 4
───────
  4 5 2
```

**d**
```
  3 6 8
– 1 ⭐ 1
───────
  ⭐ 2 7
```

**e**
```
  ⭐ 2 3
– 1 4 1
───────
  4 ⭐ 2
```

Slurp ... Give yourself a gold star. Careful –
if you get too clever, we might have to call you Pointy!

# Marvellous Multiples of Ten

Rabracadada!
I'm learning to subtract multiples of 10
from other numbers and knowing my
subtraction bonds has really helped!

Look at the patterns in these,
they should help you too!

| | | |
|---|---|---|
| 12 – 5 = 7 | 9 – 3 = 6 |
| 120 – 50 = 70 | 90 – 30 = 60 |
| 1200 – 500 = 700 | 94 – 30 = 64 |

Cabradababa! It's crystal clear!

## Task 1   Oh dear, it's easy to get in a muddle. Can you answer these?

**a** 11 – 6 =
110 – 60 =
1100 – 600 =

**b** 15 – 9 =
150 – 90 =
1500 – 900 =

**c** 17 – 8 =
170 – 80 =
1700 – 800 =

**d** 12 – 6 =
120 – 60 =
1200 – 600 =

## Task 2   Oh no, these look a bit more difficult – write the answers if you can.

**a** 12 – 9 =
120 – 90 =
122 – 90 =

**b** 13 – 4 =
130 – 40 =
133 – 40 =

**c** 15 – 8 =
150 – 80 =
156 – 80 =

**d** 16 – 9 =
160 – 90 =
167 – 90 =

**e** 14 – 8 =
140 – 80 =
145 – 80 =

**f** 11 – 5 =
110 – 50 =
118 – 50 =

**Task 3** I've been clumsy and knocked these crystal seesaws off balance. To make them level, the sum on each side has to have the same answer. Here's one I've done already. Can you write in the missing numbers for the others?

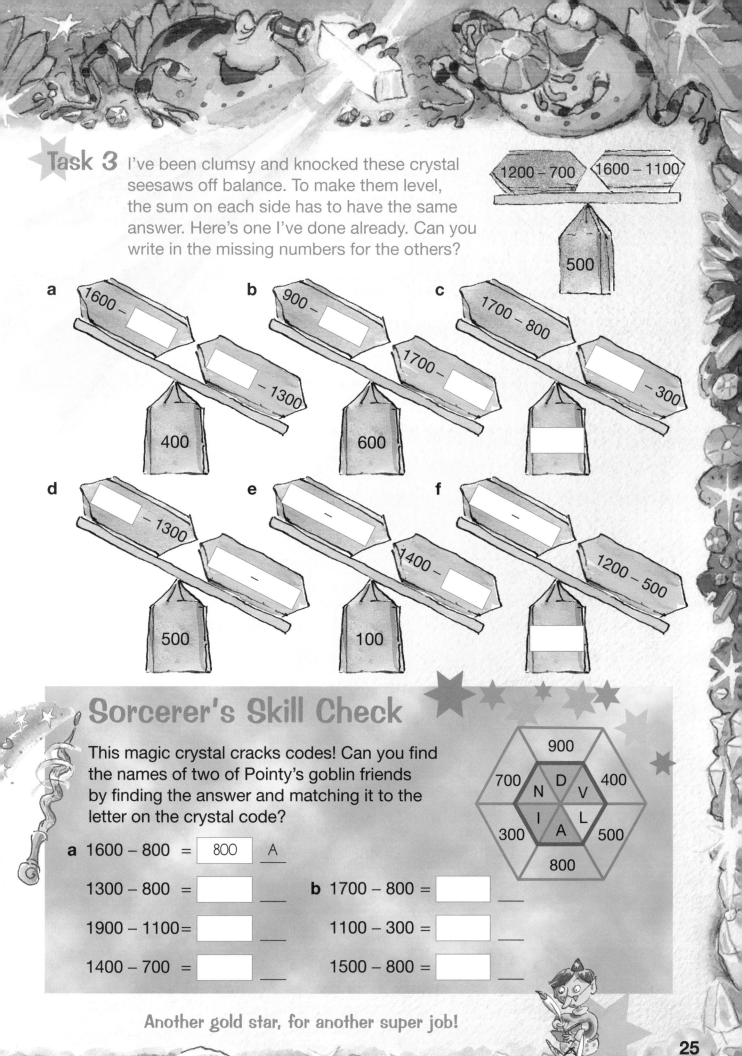

1200 – 700    1600 – 1100

500

**a** 1600 – [ ]    [ ] – 1300    400

**b** 900 – [ ]    1700 – [ ]    600

**c** 1700 – 800    [ ] – 300    [ ]

**d** [ ] – 1300    [ ]    500

**e** [ ] – [ ]    1400 – [ ]    100

**f** [ ] – [ ]    1200 – 500    [ ]

## Sorcerer's Skill Check

This magic crystal cracks codes! Can you find the names of two of Pointy's goblin friends by finding the answer and matching it to the letter on the crystal code?

900
700   N   D   V   400
300   I   A   L   500
800

**a** 1600 – 800 = [ 800 ]  A

1300 – 800 = [ ]  __

1900 – 1100 = [ ]  __

1400 – 700 = [ ]  __

**b** 1700 – 800 = [ ]  __

1100 – 300 = [ ]  __

1500 – 800 = [ ]  __

Another gold star, for another super job!

25

# Conjuring Change

Grub's up! Let's buy dinner!

Burp! Our lunch cost 63p and we gave £1.
This is how we counted out the change.

Always start with the lowest value coins.

63p → 65p → 70p → 80p → £1

(2p) + (5p) + (10p) + (20p) = | 37p change |

The change is 2p + 5p + 10p + 20p = 37p.

Is it time for a snooze yet?

**Task 1** Slurp … Use our method for counting change for each of these. Write in the missing coins and amounts.

**a** 78p → 80p → £1

(___p) + (___p) = | ____p change |

**b** 72p → ___p → ___p → ___p → £1

(1p) + (2p) + (5p) + (20p) = | ____p change |

**Task 2** We're hungry again, so we'll leave you to write in the missing coins and work out the total amount of change we got from £5.

**a** £4.46 → £4.48 → £4.50 → £5

(___p) + (___p) + (___p) = | ____p change |

**b** £1.99 → £___ → £___ → £5

(1p) + (£1) + (£2) = | £____ change |

26

**Task 3** Brain cell alert! Pointy has given us £2. How much change will we get for each of these?

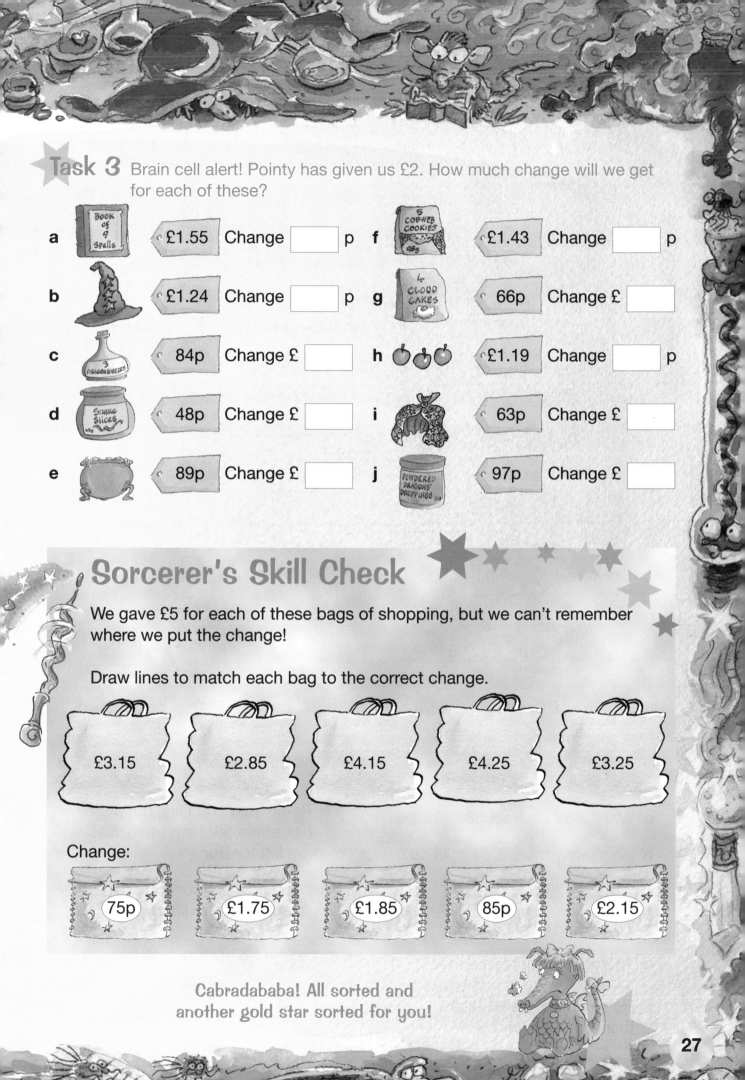

a  £1.55  Change [    ] p

b  £1.24  Change [    ] p

c  84p  Change £ [    ]

d  48p  Change £ [    ]

e  89p  Change £ [    ]

f  £1.43  Change [    ] p

g  66p  Change £ [    ]

h  £1.19  Change [    ] p

i  63p  Change £ [    ]

j  97p  Change £ [    ]

# Sorcerer's Skill Check

We gave £5 for each of these bags of shopping, but we can't remember where we put the change!

Draw lines to match each bag to the correct change.

£3.15    £2.85    £4.15    £4.25    £3.25

Change:

75p    £1.75    £1.85    85p    £2.15

Cabradababa! All sorted and another gold star sorted for you!

# Apprentice Wizard Challenge 2

**Challenge 1**  Write the answers.

> Remember – begin with brackets! Super!

a  (16 – 5) + 3  =

b  (15 + 6) – 9  =

c  (12 + 4) – (9 – 5)  =

d  12 + (7 – 5)  =

e  (13 – 7) + (14 + 5) =

f  (7 + 9) + (19 – 5)  =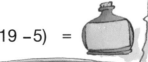

**Challenge 2**  Write the differences between these pairs of frogs.

a   63 g  84 g

Difference _____ g

b   39 g  71 g

Difference _____ g

c   56 g  37 g

Difference _____ g

d   92 g  49 g

Difference _____ g

**Challenge 3**  Read these carefully and write the answers.

a  What is 52 subtract 38?  _____

b  How many more is 61 than 49?  _____

c  What is 43 take away 27?  _____

d  What is 28 fewer than 59?  _____

e  There are 28 goblins and 44 elves hiding in a forest. How many more elves are there than goblins?  _____

f  Pointy had 100 flies, but Mugly has eaten 38. How many flies are left for Bugly?  _____

g  Draw a circle round the two lily pads with a difference of 12.

32  33  31  21  23  22

## Challenge 4 Answer these sums.

a   5 8
  − 2 6
  _____

b   9 3
  − 5 1
  _____

c   8 2
  − 4 8
  _____

d   7 4
  − 3 6
  _____

e   1 4 7
  − 8 3
  _____

f   2 9 1
  − 1 8 4
  _____

g   3 4 6
  − 2 7 1
  _____

h   3 2 4
  − 1 5 7
  _____

## Challenge 5 Write the missing numbers.

a   1400 − [ ] = 600

b   [ ] − 900 = 600

c   1700 − [ ] = 800

d   [ ] − 800 = 1500

e   1200 − [ ] = 800

f   [ ] − 500 = 1400

## Challenge 6 Complete this chart to show the change Mugly and Bugly got for each meal.

| Mugly and Bugly bought | They gave | Change |
| --- | --- | --- |
| £1.23 | £1  £1 | [ ] p |
| £2.16 | £2  50p | [ ] p |
| £2.41 | £2  £1 | [ ] p |

You've earnt your last gold star! Well done!

29

# Answers

**Task 1** **a** 0 + 16  1 + 15  2 + 14  3 + 13
4 + 12  5 + 11  6 + 10  7 + 9
8 + 8

**b** 0 + 17  1 + 16  2 + 15  3 + 14
4 + 13  5 + 12  6 + 11  7 + 10
8 + 9

**c** 0 + 11  1 + 10  2 + 9  3 + 8
4 + 7  5 + 6

**d** 0 + 12  1 + 11  2 + 10  3 + 9
4 + 8  5 + 7  6 + 6

**Task 2** **a** twenty-six  **f** thirty
**b** twenty  **g** thirty-four
**c** twenty-four  **h** thirty-two
**d** twenty-eight  **i** twenty-two
**e** thirty-six  **j** thirty-eight
The secret number is twenty-one.

**Sorcerer's Skill Check**
**a** 30 + **20**  **b** **50** + 50
**25** + 25  75 + **25**
15 + **35**  **60** + 40
**22** + 28  80 + **20**
14 + **36**  **62** + 38
**9** + 41  64 + **36**
19 + **31**  **29** + 71

**Task 1** **a** 71  **f** 82
**b** 42  **g** 71
**c** 76  **h** 52
**d** 55  **i** 61
**e** 73  **j** 54

**Task 2** **a** 87  **c** 94
51  36  49  45
**b** 89
47  42

**Task 3** **a** 90  **c** 72
42  48  34  38
**b** 99
45  54

**Task 4** There are many possible answers.
Check your child's answers, making
sure that the top number is the total
of the two numbers below.

**Sorcerer's Skill Check**
These pairs should be coloured the
same: **a** and **b**, **c** and **e**, **d** and **f**.

**Task 1** **a** 51  **e** 70
**b** 37  **f** 53
**c** 47  **g** 64
**d** 55  **h** 58

**Task 2** Monday  54p
Tuesday  58p
Wednesday  62p
Thursday  64p
Friday  58p

**Task 3** There are many possible answers.
Check that your child's choice of
sweets totals 50p.

**Sorcerer's Skill Check**
Check each group of three numbers
totals 20. There are 13 plus the 2
shown.

| 8 | 4 | 6 | 7 | 7 | 5 | 2 | 3 | 8 |
|---|---|---|---|---|---|---|---|---|
| 3 | 7 | 9 | 4 | 1 | 8 | 6 | 9 | 2 |
| 9 | 3 | 1 | 3 | 5 | 2 | 6 | 2 | 3 |
| 4 | 8 | 8 | 2 | 6 | 1 | 3 | 8 | 1 |
| 1 | 9 | 5 | 6 | 9 | 5 | 2 | 5 | 7 |

**Task 1** **a** 86  **f** 151
**b** 125  **g** 162
**c** 104  **h** 162
**d** 158  **i** 161
**e** 151

**Task 2** Check that the sum your child has
written has the same answer.
**a** 143  **f** 223
**b** 124  **g** 297
**c** 159  **h** 292
**d** 193  **i** 327
**e** 219

**Sorcerer's Skill Check**
**a** 2  5  **d** 6  8
**b** 3  1  **e** 9  7
**c** 6  5

**Task 1** **a** 11  **b** 18  **c** 23
110  180  230
1100  1800  2300

**Task 2** **a** 15  **b** 11  **c** 15
150  110  150
155  112  154

**Task 3** **a** 22  **b** 23  **c** 20
220  230  200
222  233  203

**Task 4** **a** 600 ml + 900 ml = 1500 ml
**b** 1500 ml + 700 ml = 2200 ml

**Sorcerer's Skill Check**
**a** 1700 = H  **b** 1600 = S
1300 = A  1700 = H
1900 = N  1300 = A
1900 = N  1400 = R
1300 = A  1800 = O
1700 = H  1900 = N

**Task 1** **a** £1.84  **c** £3.30
**b** £3.75  **d** £2.87

**Task 2** **a** £1  50p  20p  10p  5p
**b** £2  20p  10p  5p
**c** £1  20p  20p  2p  1p
**d** £2  £1  50p  5p
**e** £2  10p  5p  2p
**f** £2  50p  20p  2p
Other combinations may be
possible if a £2 coin is allowed.

**Sorcerer's Skill Check**
Check each purse is different and
totals £3.

**Challenge 1**
**a** 23  **f** 14
**b** 12  **g** 36
**c** 19  **h** 29
**d** 23  **i** 17
**e** 18

**Challenge 2**
**a** 72  **c** 85
**b** 64  **d** 63

**Challenge 3**
**a** 39  **c** 47
**b** 52  **d** 64

**Challenge 4**
**a** 85  **f** 329
**b** 107  **g** 407
**c** 95  **h** 596
**d** 105  **i** 425
**e** 106

**Challenge 5**
**a** 2300 g  **c** 2100 g
**b** 1900 g  **d** 2200 g

**Challenge 6**
**a** 20p, 20p, 10p
**b** 20p, 20p, 20p, 5p, 5p

**Task 1** **a** 1  9
**b** 28  28
**c** 10  24

**Task 2** 42, 33, 25, 37, 30, 16, 32, 20

**Task 3** **a** 9  **d** 2
**b** 5  **e** 19
**c** 27  **f** 6

**Task 4** **a** +  +  **g** –  +
**b** –  +  **h** –  –
**c** +  –  **i** +  –
**d** –  –  **j** +  +
**e** +  –  **k** +  –
**f** +  +  **l** –  +

**Sorcerer's Skill Check**
**a** 31  **d** 18
**b** 21  **e** 18
**c** 15  **f** 21

**Task 1** **a** +2  +40  42
**b** +4  +40  44
**c** +5  +30  35

**Task 2** **a** +6  40  +20  26
**b** +8  60  +10  18
**c** +3  70  +30  33

**Task 3**
73 with 48, 67 with 42, 38 with 13,
58 with 33, 52 with 27, 41 with 16.

**Task 4** **a** 27 g  **c** 34 g
**b** 28 g  **d** 23 g

**Sorcerer's Skill Check**
**a** 15  29  26  **b** 28  39  35
26  40  37  19  30  26
19  33  30  16  27  23

**Pages 20–21**

Task 1
a 43    f 17
b 33    g 25
c 35    h 26
d 29    i 19
e 26

Task 2
a 17    f 19
b 16    g 37
c 29    h 46
d 48    i 46
e 33

Task 3 **Across**    **Down**
a 27    a 22
c 39    b 15
d 35    c 36
e 64    d 31
g 41    f 45
i 15    g 46
j 47    h 37
l 32    i 18
m 9    j 42
n 28    k 48

Sorcerer's Skill Check
a 22    c 24
b 15    d 23

**Pages 22–23**

Task 1
a 65    d 27
b 44    e 46
c 46

Task 2
a 81    d 95
b 134    e 88
c 214

Task 3
a 381    c 282
b 171

Sorcerer's Skill Check
a 7 9    d 4 2
b 0 1    e 6 8
c 5 3

**Pages 24–25**

Task 1
a 5   b 6   c 9   d 6
   50     60     90     60
   500    600    900    600

Task 2
a 3   b 9   c 7
   30    90    70
   32    93    76
d 7   e 6   f 6
   70    60    60
   77    65    68

Task 3
a 1200    1700
b 300    1100
c 900    1200
d 1800    Check answer is 500
e Check answer is 100    1300
f Check answer is 700    700

Sorcerer's Skill Check
a 800 – A    b 900 – D
   500 – L     800 – A
   800 – A     700 – N
   700 – N

**Pages 26–27**

Task 1
a 2p 20p   22p change
b 73p 75p 80p 28p change

Task 2
a 2p 2p 50p 54p change
b £2 £3   £3.01 change

Task 3
a 45p    f 57p
b 76p    g £1.34
c £1.16    h 81p
d £1.52    i £1.37
e £1.11    j £1.03

Sorcerer's Skill Check
£3.15 → £1.85
£2.85 → £2.15
£4.15 → 85p
£4.25 → 75p
£3.25 → £1.75

**Pages 28–29**

Challenge 1
a 14    d 14
b 12    e 25
c 12    f 30

Challenge 2
a 21    c 19
b 32    d 43

Challenge 3
a 14    e 16
b 12    f 62
c 16    g 33 and 21
d 31

Challenge 4
a 32    e 64
b 42    f 107
c 34    g 75
d 38    h 167

Challenge 5
a 800    d 2300
b 1500    e 400
c 900    f 1900

Challenge 6
a 77p    c 59p
b 34p

# Wizard's Certificate of Excellence

Terrific Totals

Creepy Calculations

Astonishing Addition

Dazzling Differences

Amazing Adding

Scintillating Subtraction

Wonderful Written Methods

Sparkling Subtraction

Magnificent Multiples of Ten

Marvellous Multiples of Ten

Creaking Coins

Conjuring Change

Apprentice Wizard Challenge 1

Apprentice Wizard Challenge 2

This is to state that Wizard Whimstaff awards

Apprentice —————————————————————

the title of Maths Wizard. Congratulations!

*Wizard Whimstaff*

Published 2002
10 9 8 7 6 5

Letts Educational, The Chiswick Centre,
414 Chiswick High Road, London W4 5TF
Tel  020 8996 3333   Fax  020 8742 8390
Email  mail@lettsed.co.uk
www.letts-education.com

Text, design and illustrations © Letts Educational Ltd 2002

**Author:** Paul Broadbent
**Book Concept and Development:**
Helen Jacobs, Publishing Director; Sophie London, Project Editor
**Design and Editorial:** Cambridge Publishing Management Ltd.
**Illustrations:** Mike Phillips and Neil Chapman (Beehive Illustration)
**Cover Illustration:** Neil Chapman
**Cover Design:** Linda Males

Letts Educational Limited is a division of Granada Learning Limited.
Part of Granada plc.

**British Library Cataloguing in Publication Data**

A CIP record for this book is available from the British Library.

ISBN 1 84315 093 X

Printed in Italy

Colour reproduction by PDQ Digital Media Solutions Ltd, Bungay, Suffolk

*Handwritten annotations (top):*

- Timing — clarity - dont press 2 keys at
- Fingering     the same time...!
- Note Accuracy
  Chromatic Scale - series of semitones

# Tuneful Graded Studies

*Handwritten (left margin):*
revise
A, B, D, E Major (Flat)
- C G F Minor

## Arranged by
## DOROTHY BRADLEY

*Handwritten annotations:*
G Minor - (harmonic) - same going up and going down - check...
F Minor - do  relative of A flat                          end on 4th finger (?)
     - check fingering    └→ same coming down as going up (harmonic) check book
_ Minor

## FOREWORD

Book 3 opens with two very useful, short agility studies for keeping fingers in trim, and these are followed by an exceedingly valuable series dealing with interpretative and tecchnical points in a most interesting manner. Legato against staccaato, melody and accompaniment, contractions and skips, various types of broken chords, more detail in scale and passage-work, grace notes, syncopation, phrasing and style. Special attention is given to left hand independence. Throughout this fine series, great attention has een given to very gently progressive grading, to the tunefulness and attractiveness of the music, so that the studies are a pleasure to practise. The editing provides real phrasing-the slurs always have definite meaning, and this helps rhythmic movement-adequate fingering, attractive layout and suitablility for small hands.

The spacing and general production is clear and inviting.

*Handwritten (left margin):*
add
arpeggios

revise as
HW

*Handwritten annotations:*
* G Minor (2 flats) going up - Harmonic
  "  "  raise 6th + 7th going up - Melodic - (Eb becomes E nat)
  normal coming down                          D.B.
b
(E Maj) C - Minor - Harmonic - Harmonic - Bb becomes B nat so E flat going up then all
                              → Thumb on D                flats coming down
  *  └→ Melodic version - just Eb going up but 3 black keys coming
                                                              down

Bb + Eb + 2 relative minor scales above

## BOSWORTH
**14-15 Berners Street,**
London W1T 3LJ, UK.

E Minor

# TUNEFUL GRADED STUDIES

**VARIOUS COMPOSERS**

*Selected by* DOROTHY BRADLEY

## CONTENTS

# Agility for the Weaker Fingers, Right Hand

Both this Study and the next are short and fairly easy, and for that reason they make
an excellent preliminary canter for keeping the fingers in trim at each daily practice. Right
hand part of No. 1 to be played by finger touch, with finger tips firm enough to transmit energy
to the keys. There is no break in the succession of sounds throughout. L.H. intervals and chords,
played by hand *plus* forearm touch, must be precisely timed. It is worth while practising until
a considerable speed is easy.

CZERNY

# Left Hand Scales

Be careful with timing of L.H. notes following the semiquaver rest, and of R.H. following
the quaver rest. Rhythmic progression must be constantly forward to first beat of following bar.

CZERNY

B. & Co. Ltd. 19777

Made in England
Tous droits d'exécution réservés

# Cantabile Melody, Phrasing

This should sing with a pure tone and a beautiful breadth of phrasing as though played by a violin. Gently mark the accents in L.H. accompaniment. Play the semibreve (C) in bars 7, 15 and 17 with good tone, so that it will sing through the bar, but avoid any kind of harshness in the louder notes at any point. Pay great attention to phrasing and all small details — as the treatment of rests and slurs in bar 3, the small slurs in bars 10, 11, and the contrasts of tone in last four bars.

LOESCHHORN

B. & Co Ltd. 19777

Dominant 7ᵗʰ in F → to perfect cadence

Dynamics —[ff - ti mp p pp]
Articulation (.staccato, legato )

# Melody and Accompaniment in the Same Hand

Two most important things must be aimed for here. First to hold all melody notes for
their full value, while the quavers are played within that value; next to make sure that the
melody notes have more tone amount, and of a more singing quality, than the light accompaniment notes. See that the keys are controlled right through to sound, and not 'hit'. Let arm
weight help a rather clinging finger for the singing notes — but don't flop on the keys. Whilst
resting lightly on each melody note after it has sounded, play the quavers with finger *legato* touch.
L.H. notes — built on chord shapes — must have nicely rounded tone to support the melody.

Mostly quaved (RH)

KOHLER

**Allegro moderato** ♩ = 152-160

held thru bar

6

## Melody and Accompaniment in Left Hand

This has similar features to No.4, but here the melody is at fifth finger side of L.H., and many of the sustained notes are crotchets instead of minims— the reason will be seen if the accompaniment notes are studied carefully. There is also melody in upper notes of R.H. chords and intervals which must sing nicely. Keep L.H. notes perfectly even and attend to changes in tone amount in both hands.

KOHLER

# Independent Movement, Legato against Staccato

Care should be taken with the rhythmic flow of the music — two in the bar, with nearly all phrases beginning on the last quaver, or last but one, of the bar and leading smoothly to following accent. See that the melody is *legato,* with phrasing and small breaks neatly timed, and attend to the details of slurred and *staccato* notes in the accompaniment.

C. MAYER

# For Right Hand Weaker Fingers

Every note and every finger should be "thought", so that attention is given to the clean playing of each sound. To be played very rhythmically with finger touch in R.H., and hand touch in L.H. Notice the sustained notes in last four bars.

CZERNY

# Broken Chords, Right Hand

See that the arm is well balanced to bring R.H. over it's keys, also that the forearm is free rotatively to help towards the next key to be played. This does not mean that the arm must wobble— there need be very little actual movement, but it must not pull against the fingers. Think forward to the beginning of each next group, and forward to the accents, so that the flow of notes will be continuous. L.H. notes must sing with good supporting tone.

KOHLER

B. & Co. Ltd. 19777

# Broken Chords, Left Hand

The hints for No. 8 apply equally to this for reverse hands. Attend to tone gradations.

KOHLER

# Contrasts in Touch

This should sound light, but not tinkling, and great care should be taken with contrasts in tone between the different sections, also to progression of the two semiquavers to the following longer note throughout. The forearm should be lightly balanced so that the hand may move freely to its different keyboard positions. L.H. minims must sing well through the bar. The mood is merry, carefree.

STAMATY

# Double Thirds, Legato

Excepting in the last bar but one, all the note groups lie in one handful. The hand should be well curved, so that the finger tips can transmit energy to the keys and easily transfer their weight to the next set of fingers. The notes must enter quietly after the semiquaver rest, the middle note of each group of three to be more important than those on either side; but attention should be given to the different tone levels — as between bars 1−4, and 5−8 etc.

DUVERNOY

# Double Notes, Legato and Staccato

## THE TWO TRUMPETS

Here we have not only different intervals, but also different treatment of the notes within each phrase — legato and staccato. Slurred notes should be played by weight transfer touch, and staccato notes by hand touch with fingers neatly prepared to select the correct keys. The title will suggest the full and direct kind of tone to be aimed for, and the sturdy rhythmic movement.

STAMATY

B.& Co.Ltd. 19777

# Left Hand Agility, Scales and Arpeggios

This should be practised slowly at first, with attention given to clear articulation of every note. Afterwards it should be worked up to a good degree of brilliance. Notice the exact values of R.H. notes, and whether they are *staccato* or not.

Allegro ♩=104-112

CZERNY

13

# Finger Agility for Both Hands

Brilliant finger-touch, helped by the hand, is required for this, with great attention to rhythmic progression to the beginning of each beat.    All *staccato* marks should be carefully observed and *staccato* chords should be quite crisp.

CZERNY

# Contrasts in Touch → legato vs staccatto

Great care should be taken with the matching of tone where the two hands share
the prominence, and to rhythmic progression to the accents.

LOESCHHORN

# Slurred Couplets

Notice that this is in duple time, not quadruple, and the rhythmic movement should be rather cheerful, not dragging. The first note of each slurred couplet is played by weight touch — lapsed weight of the arm, with fingers and hand braced sufficiently to carry through into and *with* the key; the second note is played by passing-on touch, not by a separate impulse. See that this second note is lightly tapered in tone, not "kicked" off. Attend to tone gradations over and above these details of slurs: thus each second bar is stronger than the first, with tone tapered at end of phrase.

STAMATY

# For the Weaker Fingers of Both Hands

Keep the semiquavers absolutely equal in time throughout; have finger tips prepared over their keys, and keep fingers firm at top phalanx so as to transmit energy to the keys. Care should be taken to use the exact fingering marked, and special attention given to bars 3, 5, 7, 11, 13, and wherever contractions occur. Notice the difference between *legato* and *staccato* in the melodic figures — bars 1-8, compared with 9-14 etc. (L.H.)

DUVERNOY

# Neatness and Rhythmic Precision in Passage-Playing

This should be very rhythmical, the tafa-te-tafatefe figure exactly timed, and care should be taken to get the accent on the first note of the bar, with tone tapered to the quaver. L.H. accompaniment has a little melodic detail which should sing quietly. Imagine it played by a string instrument.

STAMATY

# Extended Broken Chords, Right Hand

Right hand part is played by finger touch (with the hand helping) plus rotation which may be
overdone in the early stages of practice, but should hardly be visible when the study becomes easy.

KOHLER

8 semi quavers | G C E G

B. & Co.Ltd 19777

# Extended Broken Chords, Left Hand

See notes for No.19, which apply here to left hand. In both studies the chords played by the other hand must have good singing tone and be well sustained.

KOHLER

& Co. Ltd. 19777

# Extended Broken Chords, with more Detail

Similar to No. 19 in technical features, but with more detail in keyboard movement, and in
the L.H. melody.  Notice that it is in duple time and moves smoothly and merrily.

BERTINI

B. & Co. Ltd. 19777

## Detail in Melody and Accompaniment, Clean Attack

The great points here are (a) to keep melody notes sounding during the playing of lighter notes in the same hand; (b) to see that melody and accompaniment together form an even triplet group in bars 5-8, etc; (c) to enter with clean attack on notes following rests or tied notes—as bars 2, 9, 10, and similar places; (d) to see that L.H. staccato notes in bars 7, 8, 15, 16, enters at its exact time spot and forms part of the melodic line; (e) to play the sf. notes with decision; (f) attend to contrasts in tone, and give attention to *singing* tone in those bits of L.H. melody — bars 19–20 and 23–28;

HELLER

# Contractions and Skips, Neat Fingerwork

See that the arms are lightly balanced and fingers prepared well over the keys, so that each sequential group can easily be played without break to the light *staccato* kick-off at the end of each phrase. Single *staccato* notes to be played with hand touch aided by forearm rotation.

Allegro ♩ = 108-112

HELLER

B. & Co. Ltd. 19777

# Rhythmical Scales, Agility for Both Hands

A fine study for getting equality of touch in all fingers of both hands, and for the acquirement of endurance in quickly moving passages. To be played very rhythmically.

DUVERNOY

## Rhythmic Precision in Compound Time

Great care should be taken with the rhythmic movement of weak notes to strong and short to long, and to forward progression to each phrase end — bars 4, 8, 12, etc.— clearly shown by phrase marks; also to contrasts in tone amount as between $f$ and $p$ — bars 1—8 and last quaver of bar 8 to 16, and similar places. All the ornaments are played rapidly, beginning *on* the beat.

STAMATY

# GABRIEL'S OBOE

## MUSIC BY ENNIO MORRICONE

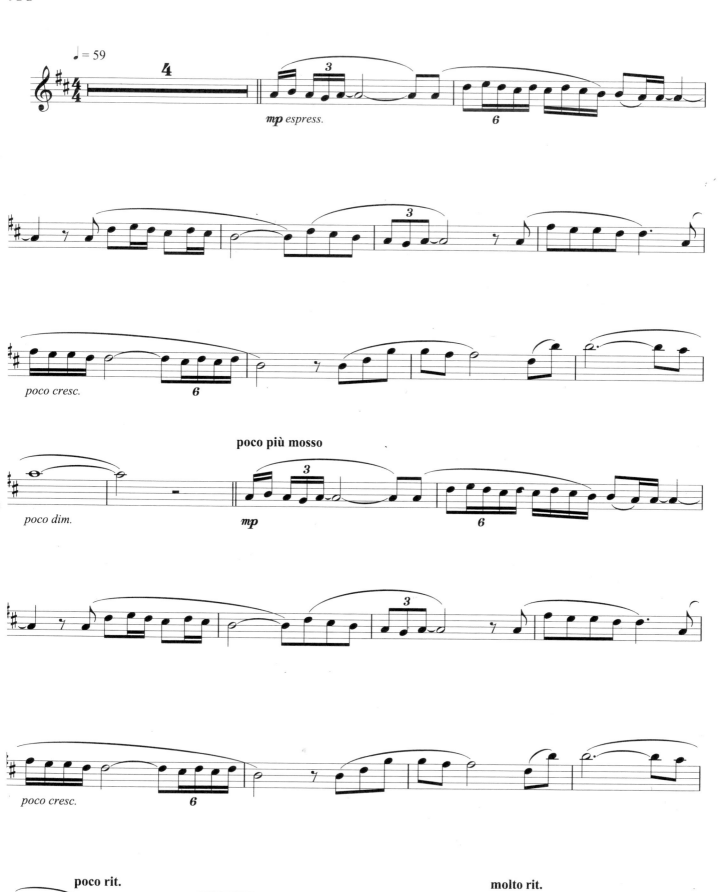

HAL • LEONARD®
CORPORATION
7777 W. BLUEMOUND RD. P.O. BOX 13819 MILWAUKEE, WI 53213

HLE90004684

ISBN 978-1-78038-991-2

9 781780 389912

# Grace Notes, Acciaccatura, Mordent

The *acciaccatura* is played very rapidly – taking no appreciable time – and throws an accent upon the principal note. The ornament in bars 19, 27, etc., a *mordent* written out in full, also begins on the beat, the first two notes played very rapidly so that the whole group goes into the value of the first bass note. Attend to all details of slurs and *staccato*. The whole effect should be lively and dainty.

CZERNY

## Neat Phrasing, Bright Rhythm

Attend to exact timing of the entry of every note, and to details of staccato and quiet ends of phrases, as in bars 4, 8, 24. Let minims in L.H. sing out nicely and keep the quavers smooth and quiet.

CZERNY

B. & Co. Ltd. 19777

# Phrasing and Style, Syncopation

Be very careful with the correct value of dotted notes, and see that the short note hops directly to the following staccato quaver. Do not lel the special accent on syncopated notes disturb the ordinary first beat accent in L.H.

STAMATY

## Left Hand Fluency

BERENS

Printed and bound in Great Britain by
Caligraving Limited Thetford Norfolk